GrueSome AND GROSS

Sticker and Activity Fun

Bodies

igloobooks

POOL OF WEE

Johnny has jumped into the pool after a toddlers' swimming lesson and is trapped by streams of wee. Use the clues to help him escape the smelly pool.

CLUES

Down 6

Right 2

Up 5

Right 2

Down 4

Right 2

Down 1

SNOTTY ONE OUT

Look at these hideously ugly faces and work out which of them is the odd one out. Make sure you don't get too close!

2

ANSWERS ON PAGE 16

LOOSE LIMBS

Draw a line between each pair of horrible, diseased limbs.
Which of them doesn't have a match?

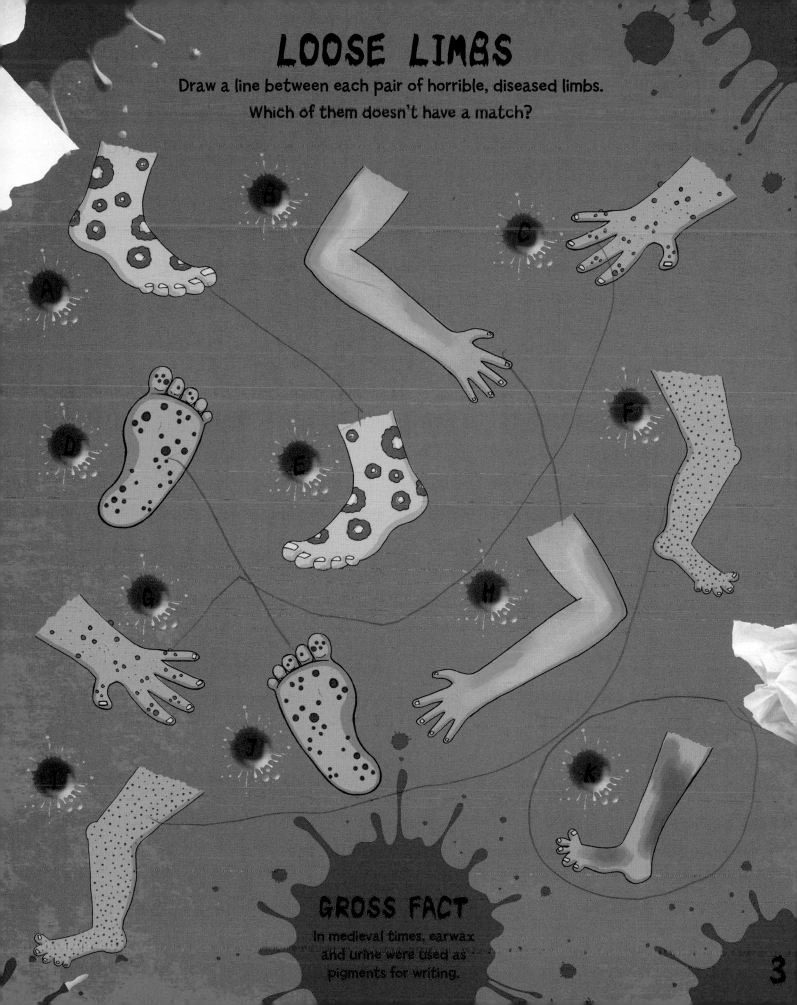

GROSS FACT

In medieval times, earwax
and urine were used as
pigments for writing.

WHAT GOES IN...

... must come out! Match these delicious dinners with
the disgusting poos that they have created.

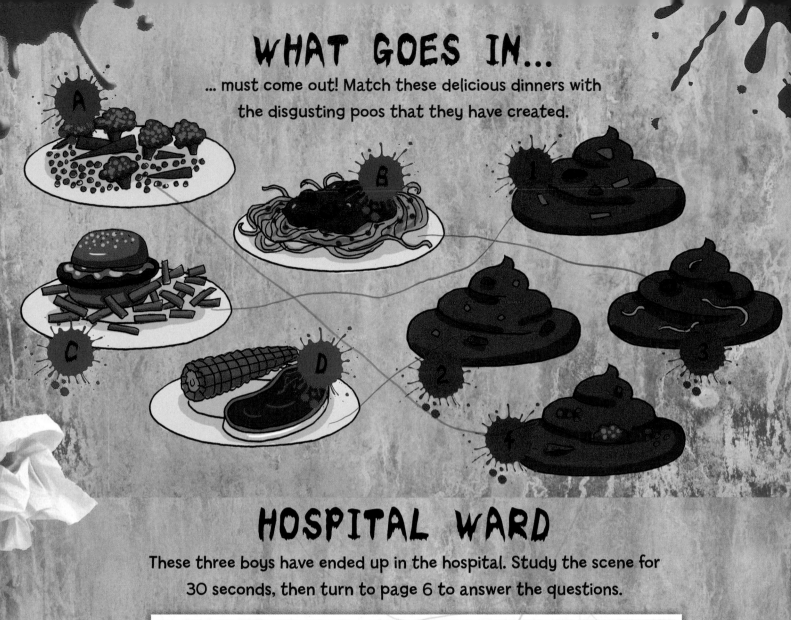

HOSPITAL WARD

These three boys have ended up in the hospital. Study the scene for
30 seconds, then turn to page 6 to answer the questions.

4

FOUL FOOD FIND

Someone has been sick all over the living room floor. How many of each piece of food can you find? Write your answers in the boxes.

12

6

9

GROSS FACT
Sick has an acid content, which wears away teeth as it passes through the mouth.

15

10

8

5

MEMORY TEST QUESTIONS

1) How many bottles of medicine are in the scene?

5 bottles

2) What is hanging on the wall above the middle bed?

~~one blood~~ picture of sore

3) What is the boy in the left-hand bed doing?

sneezing

4) What piece of furniture is placed in front of the right-hand bed?

Draw

WHO FARTED?

One of these boys has let loose a smelly fart! Follow the lines from the boys to find out which of them is the culprit.

A

B

C

D

ANSWERS ON PAGE 16

SPIT RIVER RAPIDS

These boys are seeing whose spit floats down the river the fastest. Which of their spits has the least reeds and rocks to dodge and will reach the end first?

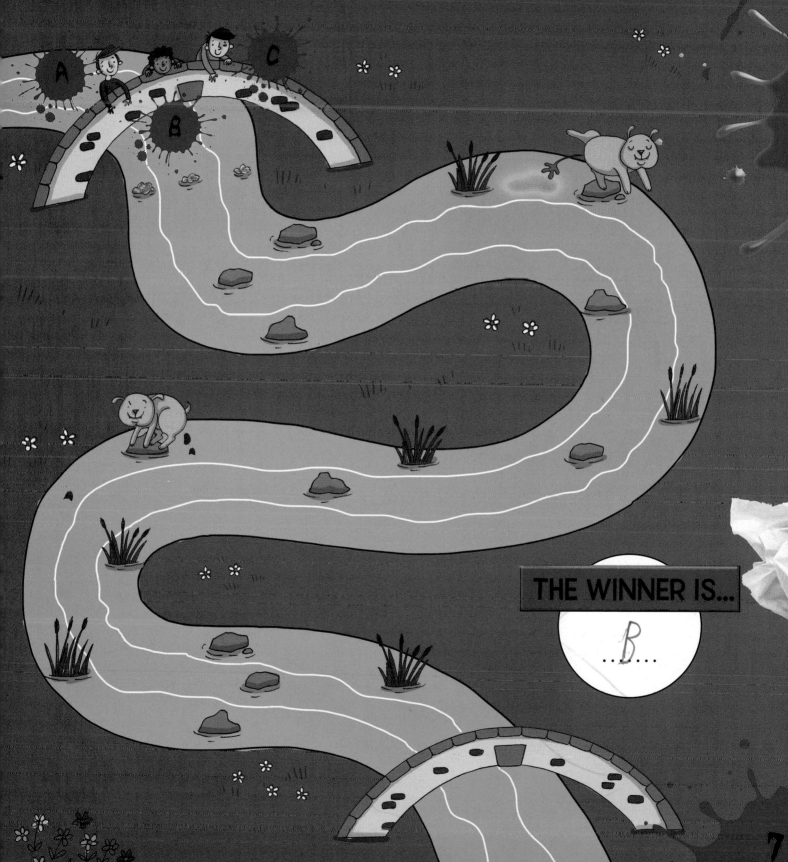

THE WINNER IS...

B

VIRUS OUTBREAK

There is a nasty virus going around the town.

Will you be able to cure each virus strand and stop the outbreak?

GAME RULES

1) You will need a friend and a dice to play this game. Each player must choose a sticker of the doctor from the sticker sheet and attach it to a coin to use as a counter.

2) Players must take it in turns to roll the dice and move their counter the correct number of spaces around the board.

3) To finish the game, each player must land on the viruses to cure them. Players must stop when they reach an orange virus space and roll the required number on the space to cure that virus. Once the correct number has been rolled, players may continue around the board from the virus space.

4) The winner of the game is the first player to reach the final space after curing each of the viruses.

START

1

2

3

STOP

Roll a 4 to cure the purple virus

17

16

Get your skates on and move forward 3 spaces.

19

20

21

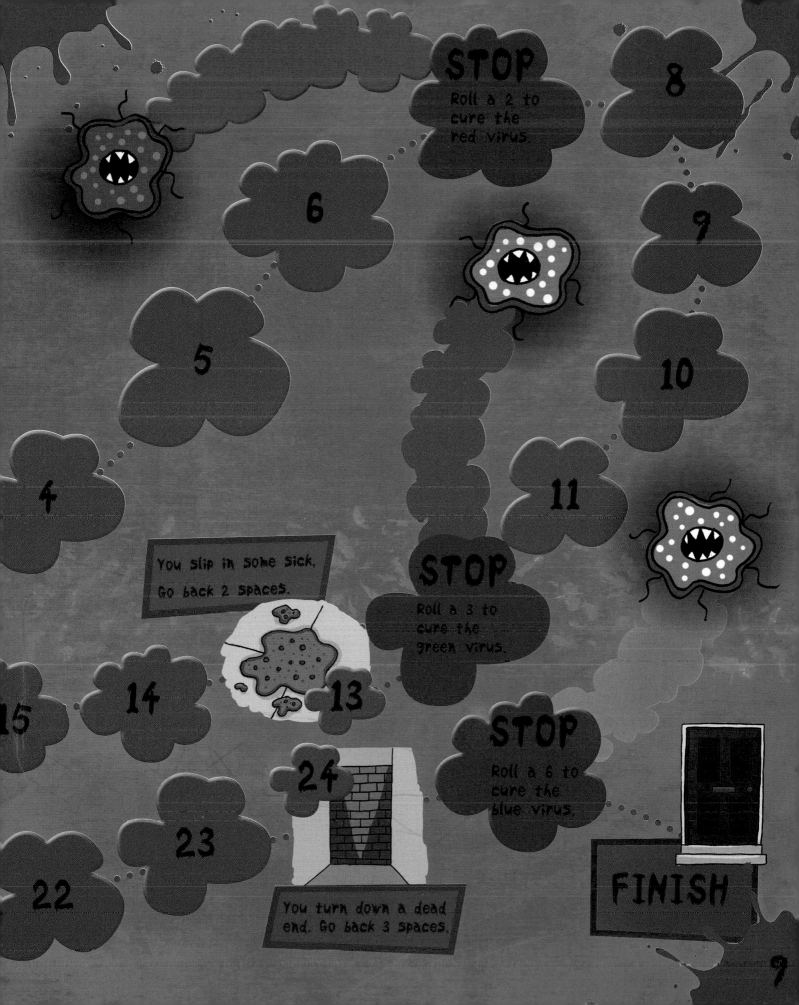

GROSS BODY SUDOKU

Match the yucky pictures to the gaps in the grid so that there is only one of each image in any row, or column.

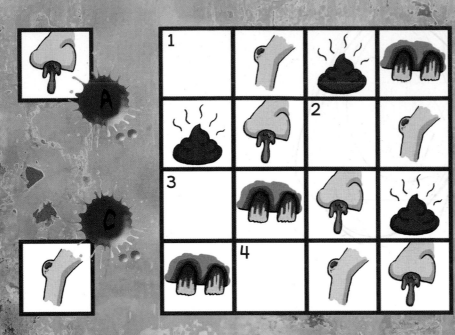

MISSING THE TARGET

Someone has missed the toilet and left splashes of wee all over the toilet mat. Which of the bingo cards matches the pattern of splashes around the carpet.

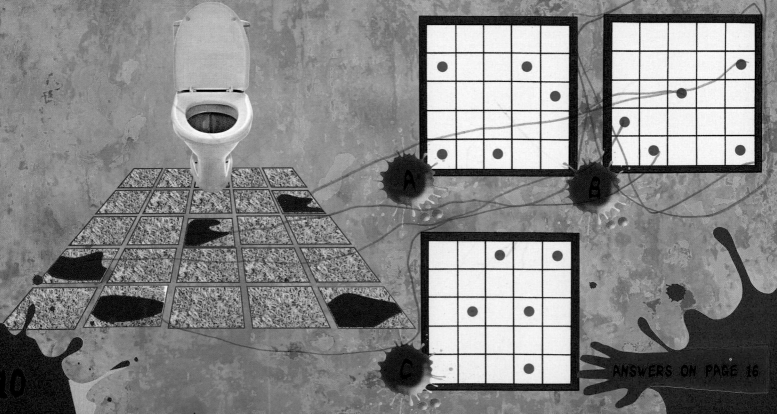

ANSWERS ON PAGE 16

10

SEWER MAZE

The toilet empties all of the poo and wee into the sewers. Draw a line through the sewer maze, avoiding the blockages to deposit the waste at the reservoir.

START

RESERVOIR

REVOLTING ROWS

These horrible body parts appear in the same order in both rows.
Fill in the gaps in the sequences with stickers from your sticker sheet.

  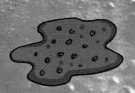  

ORGAN SHADOWS

These organs are all found in the human body.
Match each of the organs to the correct shadow.

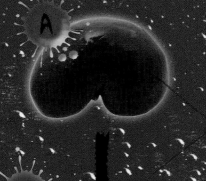 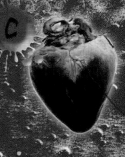 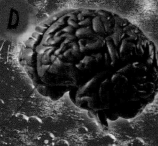 

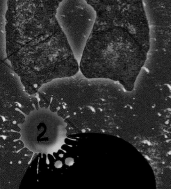

ANSWERS ON PAGE 16

SICK MAN STICKER PICTURE

Use the stickers on your sticker sheet to add various ailments and injuries to this unlucky man.

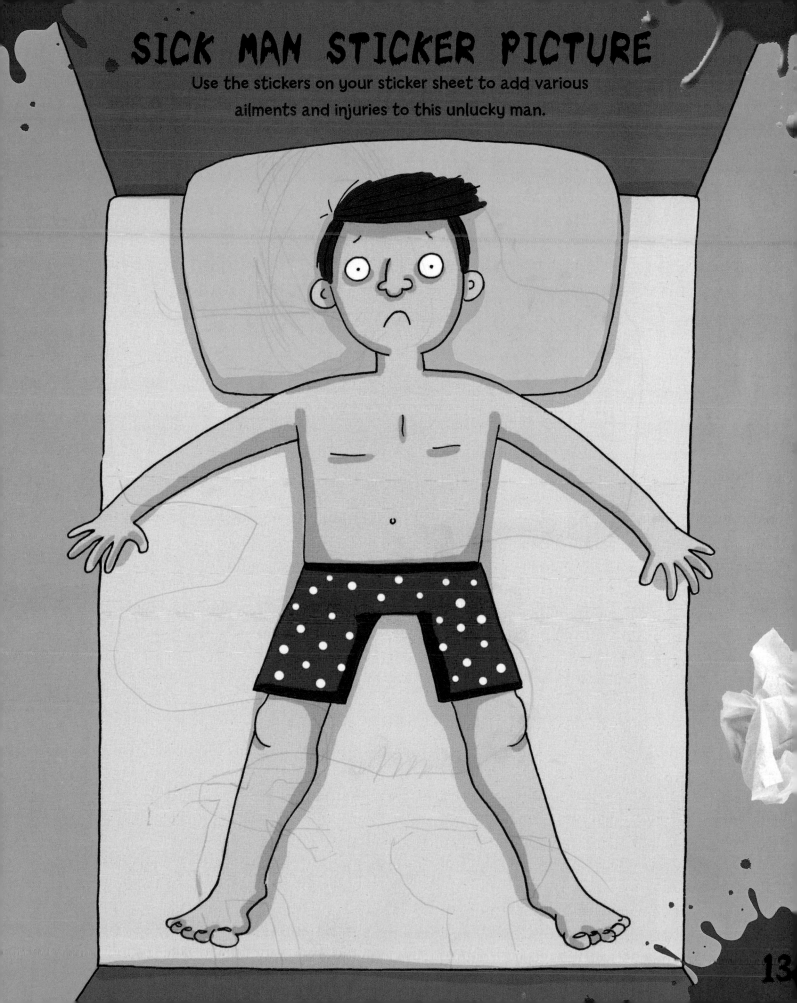

WHAT A MESS!

Someone has left an awful mess in the toilet.
Work out who the culprit is from the clues below.

CLUES

The culprit...

1) ... is wearing blue shoes

2) ... has a green top

3) ... has red trousers

4) ... has brown hair

DOT-TO-SNOT

Join the two sets of dots to find out who is covering the bathroom in a
layer of snot. Decorate the finished scene with your best pencils.

ANSWERS ON PAGE 16

NAUGHTY DOGS

These mischievous mutts are making a mess of the garden.

Circle the eleven differences in the bottom picture.

ANSWER PAGE

Page 2
POOL OF WEE:

SNOTTY ONE OUT: Odd one out is D

Page 3
LOOSE LIMBS: A-E, B-H, C-G, D-J, F-I
Odd one out is K

Page 4
WHAT GOES IN...: A-4, B-3, C-1, D-2

Page 5
FOUL FOOD FIND:
12 Gummy Bears, 7 Carrots, 9 Pizza Crusts,
8 Prawns, 10 Pastas, 16 Peas and Sweetcorn

Page 6
MEMORY TEST QUESTIONS:
1) Five 2) Picture frame 3) Sneezing 4) A cabinet

WHO FARTED?: Boy C

Page 7
SPIT RIVER RAPIDS: Boy B

Page 10
GROSS BODY SUDOKU: A-1, B-4, C-3, D-2

MISSING THE TARGET: Card B

Page 11
SEWER MAZE:

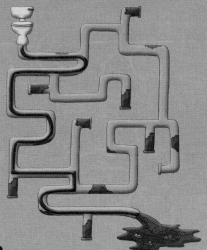

Page 12
REVOLTING ROWS:

ORGAN SHADOWS: A-2, B-1, C-4, D-3

Page 14
WHAT A MESS!: Boy B

Page 15
NAUGHTY DOGS: